The Healing Heart

by

Barbara Meyers

To Shelley, "Best Wishes" Barbara Meyers

The Healing Heart by Barbara Meyers

2015 © Barbara Meyers
bmeyerszr1@yahoo.com

Cover Art by AJ DeBiase
Interior Design by Kimberly Burnham

ISBN-10: 193720717X
ISBN-13: 978-1-937207-17-5

Publication date: October 15, 2015

Journaling / Grief Counseling / Self-Help

Creating Calm Network Publishing Group
www.creatingcalmnetworkpublishinggroup.com

Dedication

In memory of my mother whose love, wisdom, and understanding guided me through life and now she guides me with her spirit. Love and miss you.

Acknowledgements

I would like to thank my daughter Stephanie for telling me that I can do this.

For my loving grandchildren: Nathaniel, AJ, Michael, Gavin, Zachary, and Ava.

And a special thanks to Elizabeth Lupacchino "namaste."

Table of Contents

The Healing Heart by Barbara Meyers 2

Dedication 3

Acknowledgements 4

Introduction 7

Process of This Book 8

Why I Wrote This Book 9

The Daily Process 10

The Weekly Process 11

General Words...12

   Open 12

   Happy...13

   Alive 13

   Good 14

   Love 14

   Interested 15

   Strong 15

   Angry...16

   Depressed 16

   Confused 17

Helpless 17

Positive 18

Journal Pages 19

January 20

February 37

March 53

April 70

May 86

June 103

July 119

August 136

September 153

October 169

November 186

December 202

52 Weekly Activities for Healing 219

About the Author: Barbara Meyers 225

Introduction

This journal is for anyone that has lost a loved one. There are 12 chapters - one for each month. Write or do something each day for a year. Write the ending. It is your story, your journey, and your book. Make it personal.

Process of This Book

This journal is meant to start on the date that you lost a loved one. Write as much or as little as you can. Each day will be different from another. If you have a hard time with words or feelings go to the General Words with its vocabulary section and use as many words as you like. Use each word as often as needed to express your feelings.

In the Weekly Activities section at the end of the book, there are things to do each week. They are suggestions of activities that I found very comforting in my own journey. You may choose to use them in any order you like or find your own activities and use as often as is comforting to you.

The last day (or the end of the journal) is your time to shine. You write the ending because it is your story, your journey, and your loss.

I hope this brings comfort and closure to you.

Why I Wrote This Book

I wrote this journal to help anyone that has lost a loved one. The process of grieving takes a toll on us emotionally and physically, when we experience the loss of someone that we care about,

The purpose of this book is to celebrate their life. It also can help you to keep the memories you have of what the person's life was like and what they meant to you.

When my mother passed away all the ideas I had in the weekly activities section came to me and were comforting to me. By the end of the first year, even though I lost my mother—my best friend, I felt like we went on a journey together and it was wonderful.

I hope you will get the same fulfillment as I did and find it comforting.

My condolences to you.

The Daily Process

Start the book on the date of the passing.

Keep a daily journal

Use the general words to describe your feelings.

Choose a word or several words to describe how you are feeling. You can use each word more than once.

Each calendar day has a page for you to write your thoughts and notes.

The Weekly Process

Section Two has a list of weekly things to do. You can choose any of the suggestions and use one more than once if it is helpful.

General Words

The next few pages list words that you can use as often as you need to. Use these words to start expressing how you feel. Put these words into a sentence or describe an experience or memory with the word or words you have chosen.

Open

Jubilant	Sympathetic
Understanding	Interested
Confident	Satisfied
Reliable	Receptive
Easy	Accepting
Amazed	Kind
Free	Festive
Ecstatic	Satisfied

Happy

Great	Delighted
Gay	Overjoyed
Joyous	Gleeful
Lucky	Thankful
Fortunate	Important

Alive

Playful	Frisky
Courageous	Animated
Energetic	Spirited
Liberated	Thrilled
Optimistic	Animated

Good

Calm	Quiet
Peaceful	Certain
At ease	Relaxed
Comfortable	Serene
Pleased	Free and Easy
Encouraged	Bright
Clever	Blessed
Surprised	Reassured
Content	

Love

Loving	Attracted
Considerate	Passionate
Affectionate	Admiration
Sensitive	Warm
Tender	Touched
Devoted	Sympathetic
Close	Loved
Comforted	Drawn toward

Interested

Concern	Absorbed
Affected	Inquisitive
Fascinated	Snoopy
Intrigued	Engrossed
Curious	

Strong

Impulsive	Free
Sure	Certain
Rebellious	Unique
Dynamic	Tenacious
Hardy	Secure

Angry

Irritated

Enraged

Hostile

Insulting

Sore

Annoyed

Upset

Hateful

Unpleasant

Offensive

Resentful

Inflamed

Infuriated

Cross

Worked up

Fuming

Indignant

Depressed

Lousy

Disappointed

Discouraged

Ashamed

Powerless

Diminished

Guilty

Dissatisfied

Miserable

Repugnant

Despicable

Disgusting

Terrible

In despair

Sulky

Bad

A sense of loss

Confused

Upset

Uncertain

Perplexed

Hesitant

Disillusioned

Skeptical

Misgiving

Unsure

Pessimistic

Doubtful

Indecisive

Embarrassed

Shy

Unbelievable

Distrustful

Lost

Uneasy

Tense

Helpless

Incapable

Paralyzed

Useless

Vulnerable

Forced

Despair

Distressed

Pathetic

Dominated

Alone

Fatigued

Inferior

Empty

Hesitant

Frustrated

Woeful

Tragic

Positive

Eager	Keen
Earnest	Intent
Inspired	Determining
Excited	Enthusiastic
Bold	Brave
Daring	Challenged
Optimistic	Reinforced
Confident	Hopeful

Journal Pages

Fill the following pages with love, life, and healing.

January

"January is a month of starting over. The holidays have passed and friends and families are back to a routine —be thankful and start a new."

— Barbara Meyers

What would you write if you filled in the sentence: January is a month of ... ?

"All healing is first healing the heart"

— Carl Townsend

January 1

January 2

January 3

January 4

January 5

January 6

January 7

January 8

January 9

January 10

January 11

January 12

January 13

January 14

January 15

January 16

January 17

January 18

January 19

January 20

January 21

January 22

January 23

January 24

January 25

January 26

January 27

January 28

January 29

January 30

January 31

February

"February is a month to celebrate love and loved ones."
> —Barbara Meyers

What would you write if you filled in the sentence: February is a month of ... ?

"Eventually you will come to understand that love heals everything and love is all there is"
> —Gary Zukav

February 1

February 2

February 3

February 4

February 5

February 6

February 7

February 8

February 9

February 10

February 11

February 12

February 13

February 14

February 15

February 16

February 17

February 18

February 19

February 20

February 21

February 22

February 23

February 24

February 25

February 26

February 27

February 28

February 29

March

"March is a month of quiet and planning for spring."
—Barbara Meyers

What would you write if you filled in the sentence:
March is a month of ... ?

"Healing takes courage and we all have courage even
if we dig a little to find it"

—Tori Amos

March 1

March 2

March 3

March 4

March 5

March 6

March 7

March 8

March 9

March 10

March 11

March 12

March 13

March 14

March 15

March 16

March 17

March 18

March 19

March 20

March 21

March 22

March 23

March 24

March 25

March 26

March 27

March 28

March 29

March 30

March 31

April

"April is a month of awakening and growth."
                                    —Barbara Meyers

What would you write if you filled in the sentence:
April is a month of ... ?

"Healing is a matter of time, but it is sometimes also a
matter of opportunity"
                                    —Hippocrates

April 1

April 2

April 3

April 4

April 5

April 6

April 7

April 8

April 9

April 10

April 11

April 12

April 13

April 14

April 15

April 16

April 17

April 18

April 19

April 20

April 21

April 22

April 23

April 24

April 25

April 26

April 27

April 28

April 29

April 30

May

"May is a month of watching nature come alive."

—Barbara Meyers

What would you write if you filled in the sentence: May is a month of ... ?

"Our sorrows and wounds are healed only when we touch them with compassion."

—Buddha

May 1

May 2

May 3

May 4

May 5

May 6

May 7

May 8

May 9

May 10

May 11

May 12

May 13

May 14

May 15

May 16

May 17

May 18

May 19

May 20

May 21

May 22

May 23

May 24

May 25

May 26

May 27

May 28

.

May 29

May 30

May 31

June

"June is a month of warmth." —Barbara Meyers

What would you write if you filled in the sentence: June is a month of ... ?

"Healing does not mean going back to the way things were before, but rather allowing what is now to move us close to God"

—Ram Dass

June 1

June 2

June 3

June 4

June 5

June 6

June 7

June 8

June 9

June 10

June 11

June 12

June 13

June 14

June 15

June 16

June 17

June 18

June 19

June 20

June 21

June 22

June 23

June 24

June 25

June 26

June 27

June 28

June 29

June 30

July

"July is a month of celebrations." —Barbara Meyers

What would you write if you filled in the sentence: July is a month of ... ?

"The wish for healing has always been half of health"
—Lucius Annaeus Seneca

July 1

July 2

July 3

July 4

July 5

July 6

July 7

July 8

July 9

July 10

July 11

July 12

July 13

July 14

July 15

July 16

July 17

July 18

July 19

July 20

July 21

July 22

July 23

July 24

July 25

July 26

July 27

July 28

July 29

July 30

July 31

August

"August is a month of daydreaming and the summer coming to an end." —Barbara Meyers

What would you write if you filled in the sentence: August is a month of ... ?

"I believe that imagination is stronger than knowledge. That myth is more potent than history. That dreams are more powerful than facts. That hope always triumphs over experience. That laughter is the only cure for grief. And I believe that love is stronger than death."

—Robert Fulghum

August 1

August 2

August 3

August 4

August 5

August 6

August 7

August 8

August 9

August 10

August 11

August 12

August 13

August 14

August 15

August 16

August 17

August 18

August 19

August 20

August 21

August 22

August 23

August 24

August 25

August 26

August 27

August 28

August 29

August 30

August 31

September

"September is a month of cooler nights and the smell of fall in the air." —Barbara Meyers

What would you write if you filled in the sentence: September is a month of ... ?

"You cannot be lonely if you like the person your alone with"

—Wayne Dyer

September 1

September 2

September 3

September 4

September 5

September 6

September 7

September 9

September 10

September 11

September 12

September 13

September 14

September 15

September 16

September 17

September 18

September 19

September 20

September 21

September 22

September 23

September 24

September 25

September 26

September 27

September 28

September 29

September 30

October

"October is a month of sweaters and dusting off the crock pot."

—Barbara Meyers

What would you write if you filled in the sentence: October is a month of ... ?

"For truly the way out of pain is to go deeper into it"

—Brandon Bays

October 1

October 2

October 3

October 4

October 5

October 6

October 7

October 8

October 9

October 10

October 11

October 12

October 13

October 14

October 15

October 16

October 17

October 18

October 19

October 20

October 21

October 22

October 23

October 24

October 25

October 26

October 27

October 28

October 29

October 30

October 31

November

"November is a months of giving thanks to all."
—Barbara Meyers

What would you write if you filled in the sentence: November is a month of ... ?

"Forgiveness releases you completely from your story of pain and allows you to move forward in freedom in your life"
—Brandon Bays

November 1

November 2

November 3

November 4

November 5

November 6

November 7

November 8

November 9

November 10

November 11

November 12

November 13

November 14

November 15

November 16

November 17

November 18

November 19

November 20

November 21

November 22

November 23

November 24

November 25

November 26

November 27

November 28

November 29

November 30

December

"December is a month of holiday planning and get together's."

—Barbara Meyers

What would you write if you filled in the sentence: December a month of ... ?

"Emotions are your gateway to the soul. Dive into the core of any emotion, let it overwhelm the heart of it, opening and surrendering to it"

—Brandon Bays

December 1

December 2

December 3

December 4

December 5

December 6

December 7

December 8

December 9

December 10

December 11

December 12

December 13

December 14

December 15

December 16

December 17

December 18

December 19

December 20

December 21

December 22

December 23

December 24

December 25

December 26

December 27

December 28

December 29

December 30

December 31

52 Weekly Activities for Healing

In this section there are suggestions of activities to help in your healing. Check off the ones that you do and repeat as often as you like.

1) Print any newspaper article about the person and paste it to page. Explain how you found out about them and how you felt.

2) Talk to a family member.

3) What was the person like? Write in detail.

4) What was their favorite flower? Smell it. Pick it. Plant it.

5) Wear their favorite color today.

6) Do you know their favorite kind of music? Play it. Sing it. Dance to it.

7) Celebrate their favorite holiday in your home.

8) Call, e-mail, or write to their favorite friend.

9) Visit their work place to hear people talk about or reminisce about them.

10) What was a cause that they were interested in? Volunteer some of your time or resources to support the cause.

11) What did this person pass away from? Donate to their favorite charity.

12) Do a walk-a-thon in their name or a fund raiser.

13) Gather friends, family and co-workers and tell stories.

14) Spend a day with one of their friends or a family member.

15) Watch their favorite TV show.

16) What was their favorite movie? Rent it.

17) Who was their favorite actor or actress? Did you have that in common with them? Explain.

18) Go to their favorite restaurant.

19) Recreate their favorite recipe or food.

20) What was your support through all this? Write something about your relationships to friends, family, religion, sympathy cards, etc. What or who was your support through this difficult time?

21) Find a picture of the person with or without you and paste on page.

22) Where did they live? Visit the area. Drive by.

23) Talk to a family member. Repeat this step as often as you need to.

24) Buy a card for yourself and mail it to yourself.

25) What was their favorite perfume or cologne? Go to a store and spray it on.

26) Send a birthday card to yourself on their birthday to celebrate day.

27) Name a star in the sky after them.

28) Bring their favorite dessert to work or a neighbor's house.

29) Use a rainy day to go through photo albums.

30) Take a selfie or self portrait and paste in book.

31) Bring a plate of food to an elderly neighbor.

32) Come up with something on your own.

33) Go for a walk and listen, really listen to sounds (birds, cars, people, etc.) How many different sounds can you hear?

34) Listen to music and dance. It doesn't matter how crazy you get.

35) Watch the sunset.

36) Watch the sunrise.

37) Find a butterfly and describe it in detail.

38) Listen to a bird chirping for at least 10 minutes.

39) Draw or color something on a page. No talent needed.

40) Look at the clouds until you find the shape of something.

41) Wear their favorite color again.

42) Mail a thank you card to their family member telling them how thankful you were for having this person in your life.

43) Check on someone not feeling well today.

44) Contact an old relative or friend you haven't heard from in a while.

45) Call a loved one today.

46) What was their favorite quote or saying? Write it on a page.

47) What was their favorite holiday? Describe it in detail or celebrate it their way.

48) Make a collage of this person's pictures, sayings, etc. You design it.

49) Enjoy a full moon.

50) What was their favorite season?

51) How has this journal helped you? Did you find comfort and healing? Explain.

52) You write the ending. It is your story, your journey, your book. Make it personal.

About the Author: Barbara Meyers

Barbara was born and raised in Connecticut. She lives in Stratford, a small town filled with history. The sudden death of her father at age eleven unknown to her would be the beginning of many, many painful losses in her life which would explain her amazing strength and courage. Her love and compassion towards others go without saying.

Barbara has raised three wonderful children on her own. Their God given gifts have made each of them pursue careers they love.

Barbara is a hairdresser and cosmetologist by trade. She is now a style expert at a local boutique. In her down time she is pursuing her original passion in art.

Being around people and being such a good listener, Barbara saw the need for this journal. The loss of her mother—her best friend was devastating, but her strength and faith guided her through as her mother's spirit did through this journal. She hopes you the reader find comfort through "The Healing Heart"

Made in the USA
Middletown, DE
27 October 2015